HITS OF THE  R

Wise Publications
part of The Music Sales Group
London / New York / Paris / Sydney / Copenhagen / Berlin / Madrid / Hong Kong / Tokyo

Published by
Wise Publications
14-15 Berners Street, London W1T 3LJ, UK.

Exclusive Distributors:
Music Sales Limited
Distribution Centre, Newmarket Road,
Bury St Edmunds, Suffolk IP33 3YB, UK.

Music Sales Pty Limited
Units 3-4, 17 Willfox Street, Condell Park, NSW 2200, Australia.

Order No. AM1008480
ISBN: 978-1-78305-462-6
This book © Copyright 2013 Wise Publications,
a division of Music Sales Limited.

Edited by Jenni Norey.
Cover photos: Olly Murs - Dave Hogan/Getty Images – One Direction -
Kevin Mazur/WireImage – Katy Perry - David Livingston/Getty Images –
Miley Cyrus -John Thys/AFP/Getty Images – Ellie Goulding -
Jamie McCarthy/Getty Images.

Printed in the EU.

Your Guarantee of Quality
As publishers, we strive to produce every book
to the highest commercial standards.
The music has been freshly engraved and the
book has been carefully designed to minimise
awkward page turns and to make playing from
it a real pleasure.
Particular care has been given to specifying acid-free,
neutral-sized paper made from pulps which have not
been elemental chlorine bleached.
This pulp is from farmed sustainable forests and was
produced with special regard for the environment.
Throughout, the printing and binding have been
planned to ensure a sturdy, attractive publication
which should give years of enjoyment.
If your copy fails to meet our high standards,
please inform us and we will gladly replace it.

www.musicsales.com

Blurred Lines

Words & Music by Pharrell Williams, Robin Thicke
& Clifford Harris

4

6

7

11

Clown

Words & Music by Shahid Khan, Emeli Sandé
& Grant Mitchell

1. I guess it's fun-ni-er from where you're stand - ing,

'cause from o - ver here I missed the joke.

Clear the way for my crash land - ing. I've done it a - gain,

cir - cus, cir - cus. 'Round in cir - cles, sell - ing out___ to - night.___

sell - ing out___ to - night. From a dis - tance my choice is sim-

- ple. From a dis - tance I can en - ter - tain.___

So you can see me I put

Counting Stars

Words & Music by Ryan Tedder

Late-ly I been,_ I been los-ing sleep_ dream-ing a-bout_ the things that we could be. But ba - by, I been,_ I been pray-in' hard,_ said no more count-ing dol-lars we'll be count-ing stars. Yeah, we'll be count-ing stars._

Take that mon-ey watch it burn. Sink in the ri-ver, the les - sons I learned.

C#m

Take that mon-ey watch it burn. Sink in the ri-ver, the les - sons I learned.

Take that mon-ey watch it burn. Sink in the ri-ver, the les - sons I learned.

A

F#m

D.S. al Coda

Ev - 'ry - thing that kills me makes me feel a - live.

24

Dear Darlin'

Words & Music by James Eliot, Edward Drewett
& Oliver Murs

Dear darl - in', please ex-cuse my writ - ing.

I can't stop my hands from shak - ing 'cause I'm cold and a-lone to - night.

And I miss you and noth-ing hurts like no you. And

no one un-der-stands what we went___ through.___ It was short. It was sweet. We tried.

And if my words break through the wall and meet you at your door,

all I can say is "Girl, I mean them all." Dear__ darl-

-in', please ex-cuse__ my writ-ing.___

29

Get Lucky

Words & Music by Thomas Bangalter, Pharrell Williams,
Guy-Manuel de Homem-Christo & Nile Rodgers

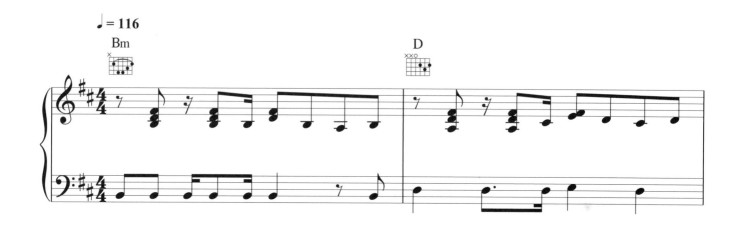

1. Like the leg-end of__ the
2. The pre-sent has__ no

We're up all night to get luck - y. We're up all night to get luck - y.

We're up all night to get luck - y. We're up all night to get luck - y.

Repeat to fade

39

Ho Hey

Words & Music by Jeremy Fraites & Wesley Schultz

How Long Will I Love You

Words & Music by Mike Scott

and lon - ger if I may.

Mm._____ Mm,_____ mm._____

How long will I love you? As long as stars are a-bove you.

I Knew You Were Trouble

Words & Music by Max Martin, Taylor Swift
& Shellback

Just Give Me A Reason

Words & Music by Alecia Moore, Jeff Bhasker
& Nate Ruess

1. Right from the start you were a thief___ you stole my heart, and I your will - ing vic -tim.

I let you see the parts of me that weren't all that pret - ty, and with

56

Let Her Go

Words & Music by Michael Rosenberg

Love Me Again

Words & Music by Stephen Booker & John Newman

1. (I) know I've done wrong, left your heart torn. Is that what dev - ils do?___

Took you so low, where on - ly fools go, I shook the an - gel in you.___

70

Mirrors

Words & Music by Justin Timberlake

1. Aren't you some-

-thin' to ad-mire_____ 'cause your shine_____ is some-thin' like a mir-ror. And I can't help but no-

(2.)- thin', an o-ri-gi-nal 'cause it does-n't seem real-ly as sim-ple. And I can't help but stare,

73

I'm look-in' right at the oth-er half of me. The va-can-cy that sat in my heart_

_____ is a space_ that you now hold.__ Show me how to fight for now_

_____ I'll tell you, ba-by, it was eas-y com-in' back in-to you once I fi-gured it out._

_____ You were right_ here all a-long._____ It's like you're my mir-

One Way Or Another
(Teenage Kicks)

Words & Music by John O'Neill, Deborah Harry
& Nigel Harrison

88

Pompeii

Words & Music by Daniel Campbell Smith

Stay

Words & Music by Justin Parker & Mikky Ekko

just some-thing you take, it's gi-ven.

2.
And I want you to stay.

Oh the rea-son I hold on.

Oh 'cause I need this hole gone.

Roar

Words & Music by Lukasz Gottwald, Bonnie McKee, Katy Perry,
Martin Max & Henry Russell Walter

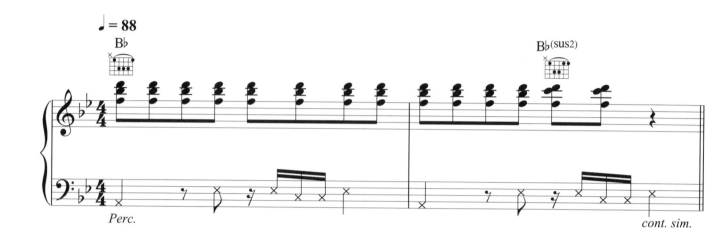

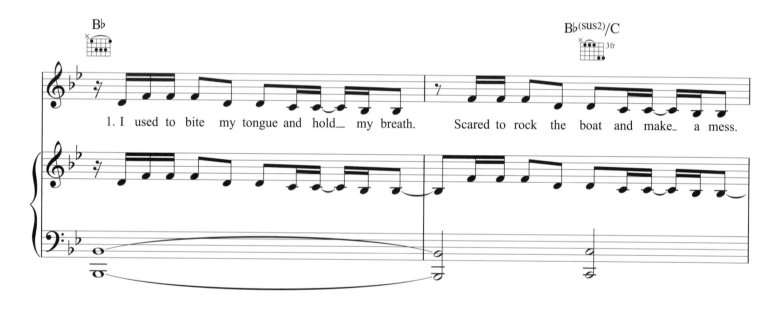

1. I used to bite my tongue and hold my breath. Scared to rock the boat and make a mess.

So I sat qui-et-ly, a-greed po-lite-ly.

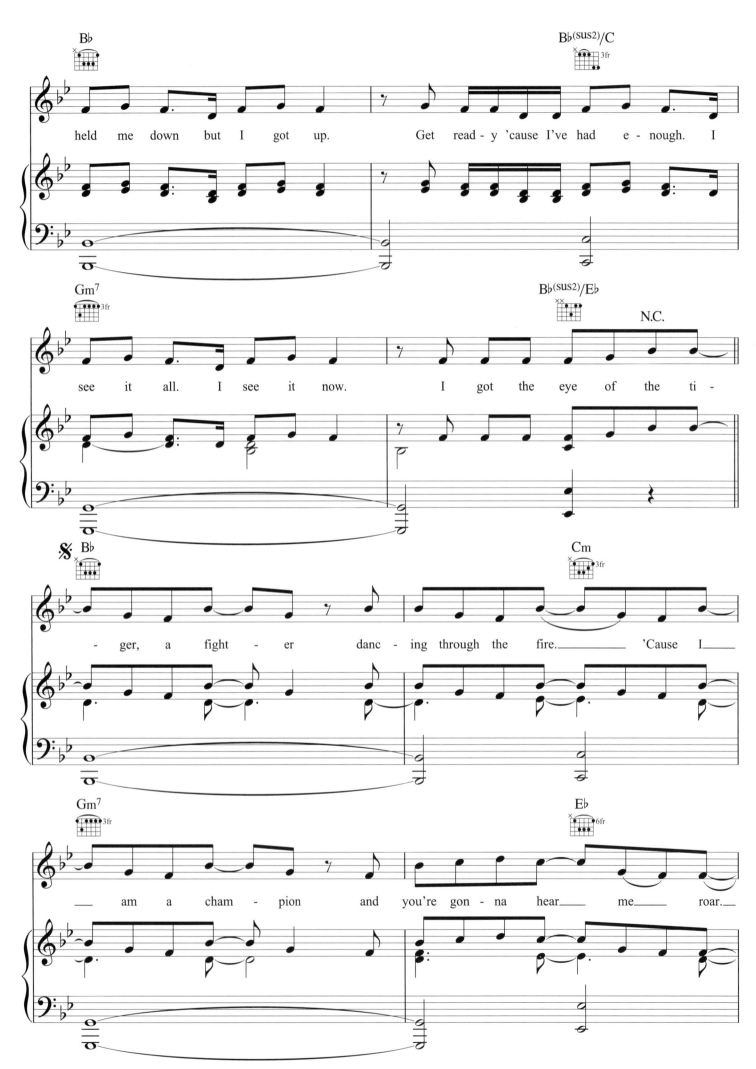

Lou - der, lou - der than the li - on. 'Cause I ___

___ am a cham - pion and you're gon - na hear ___ me ___ roar. ___ Oh, oh, oh, oh, oh. ___

Oh, ___ oh, oh, oh, oh, oh. ___ Oh, ___ oh, oh, oh, oh, oh. ___

You're gon - na hear ___ me roar. ___ Oh, oh, oh, oh, oh.

Perc.

Wrecking Ball

**Words & Music by Stephan Moccio, Sacha Skarbek, Lukasz Gottwald,
Henry Russell Walter & Maureen McDonald**

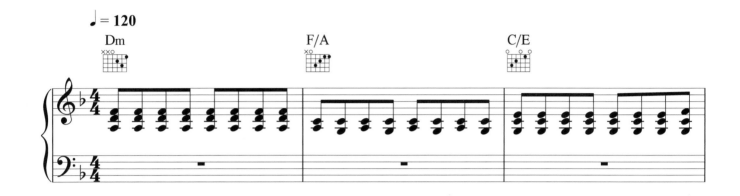

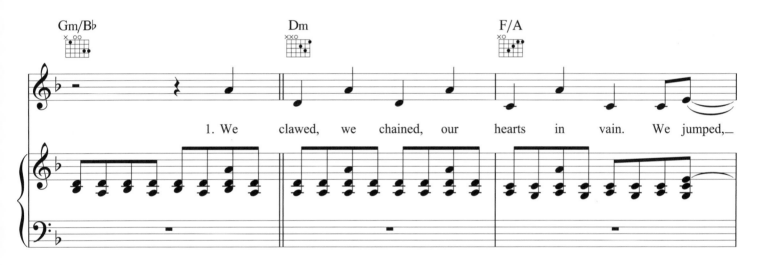

1. We clawed, we chained, our hearts in vain. We jumped,__

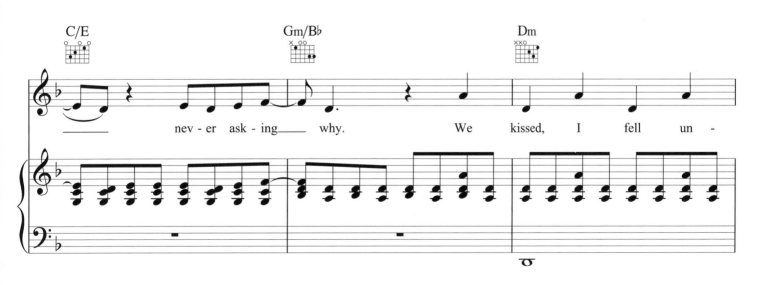

nev-er ask-ing___ why. We kissed, I fell un-

108

113

Wake Me Up

Words & Music by Aloe Blacc, Tim Bergling
& Michael Einziger

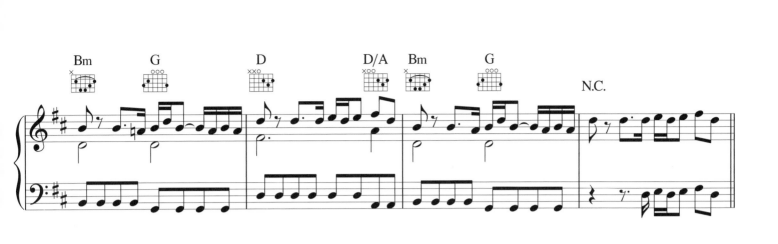

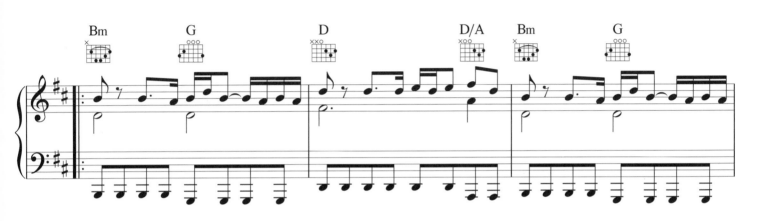

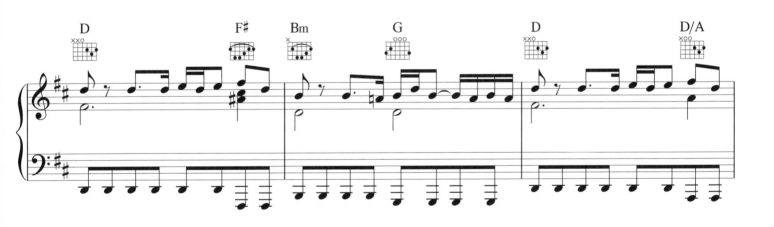

118

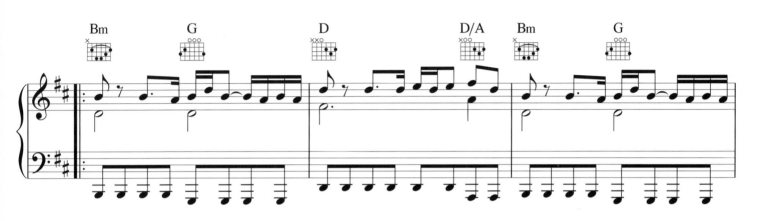

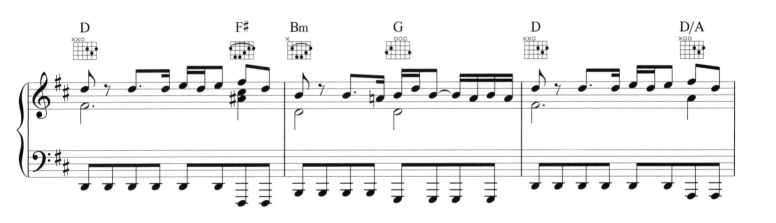

123456789